Shojo Beat

Kaze Hikaru

19

Story & Art by
Taeko Watanabe

Contents

Story Thus Far

It is the end of the Bakufu era, the third year of Bunkyu (1863) in Kyoto. The Shinsengumi is a band of warriors formed to protect the shogun.

Tominaga Sei, the daughter of a former Bakufu *bushi*, joined the Shinsengumi disguised as a boy by the name of Kamiya Seizaburo to avenge her father and brother. She has continued her training under the only person in the Shinsengumi who knows her true identity, Okita Soji, and she aspires to become a true *bushi*.

Foreign ships have appeared off the Hyogo port, demanding imperial sanction of the trade treaty. The Shinsengumi are eager to put down the foreign forces, but their orders limit them to patrolling Osaka.

Kondo sets out for Osaka with Sei and Okita but collapses from his worsening stomach. Sei pushes her way into a Shinmachi establishment to see Miyuki-dayu, the geisha that Kondo fell in love with. There, she meets Ukinosuke, a barfly who insults all *bushi* and infuriates her to no end.

Characters

Tominaga Sei
She disguises herself as a boy to enter the Mibu-Roshi.
She trains under Soji, aspiring to become a true *bushi*.
But secretly, she is in love with Soji.

Okita Soji
Assistant vice captain of the Shinsengumi and licensed
master of the Ten'nen Rishin-Ryu. He supports
the troop alongside Kondo and Hijikata and guides
Seizaburo with a kind yet firm hand.

Kondo Isami
Captain of the Shinsengumi and fourth grandmaster of
the Ten'nen Rishin-ryu. A passionate, warm and well-
respected leader.

Hijikata Toshizo
Vice captain of the Shinsengumi. He commands both
the group and himself with a rigid strictness. He is also
known as the "Oni vice captain."

Matsudaira Katamori
Lord of the Aizu-han. He is the master of the
Shinsengumi who ensures the peace in Kyoto.

Ukinosuke
A mysterious playboy who is the main customer of
Shinmachi's premier *tayu*. He seems to be a merchant
but has an air that says he is a man of greater
significance.

SEPTEMBER OF THE FIRST YEAR OF KEIO (NOVEMBER 1865).

THE OSAKA CASTLE WAS IN UTTER TURMOIL.

WE WANT THE *IMMEDIATE* OPENING OF THE HYOGO PORT AND IMPERIAL SANCTION OF THE TRADE TREATY!!

WE WILL TAKE YOU BY *FORCE* IF YOU STALL MUCH LONGER!

→ LOOSE TRANSLATION

HOW LONG DO YOU PLAN ON MAKING US WAIT?!

...IS THE MESSAGE, SIR.

THE FOREIGN FORCES SAID THAT THE DEADLINE FOR AN ANSWER IS THE 26TH!

THAT'S IN *FIVE* DAYS!

ISSUN NO OTOME NIMO BUSHI NO TAMASHII

"EVEN THE SMALL GIRL HAS THE SOUL OF BUSHI"

by Yukachin-san from TOKYO

KAZE HIKARU IROHA KARUTA

8

U...

...KINO...

...SUKE...

...SAMA !

YOU'RE FORGETTING THE "UKINO-SUKE-SAMA" PART. ♡

IF YOU COULD LEND ME MIYUKI-DAYU...

...FOR JUST A MERE FEW HOURS!!

MY BUSINESS IS A PRESSING MATTER.

UNFORTU-NATELY...

I BEG YOU...

HUH?

I WOULD WAIT FOR A FEW INCENSE STICKS,* BUT...

WHY DO YOU THINK I'M ASKING YOU?!

ARE YOU OUT OF YOUR MIND? I BOUGHT HER FOR THE WHOLE DAY AND NIGHT.

MIYUKI ?!

*Geisha time was measured by the time it took to burn incense.

10

*The lowliest of geisha who are only called on to sell their bodies.
**Short for *buzaemon*. How *bushi*, particularly those from rural roots, were referred to in *yuri* as a way to ridicule them.

13

14

He certainly flew over there!

WHAM

I'M SEIZABURO'S **MAN.**

ARE YOU A MEMBER OF THE SHINSENGUMI TOO?

I SEE. SO YOU'VE PROMISED YOURSELVES TO ONE ANOTHER.

THEREFORE, I'D APPRECIATE IT IF YOU KEPT YOUR HANDS OFF OF HIM.

W—W—WHAT ARE YOU SAYING?

I AM OKITA SOJI, CAPTAIN OF THE SHINSENGUMI FIRST TROOP!

18

*The master of the Aizu clan, Lord Matsudaira Katamori of Higo.

20

...BUT MY MASTER, KONDO ISAMI, IS A MAN OF GREAT CALIBER.

HIS GREATNESS MORE THAN COMPENSATES FOR MY SHORT-COMINGS.

YOU NEED NOT WORRY.

!!

JUST TAKE *TAYU* WITH YOU!

HA HA. I WAS JUST CAUGHT UP IN THE MOMENT...

WHY ARE YOU SPEAKING TO A MERE MERCHANT AS IF YOU SERVE HIM, OKITA SENSEI!?!

...

I'LL BE FINE.

THANK YOU.

GOOD LUCK!

I'M SORRY TO DISTURB YOU DURING YOUR LEISURE TIME.

BUT THE CLERK'S COME FOR YOU AGAIN.

WHAT IS IT, MATSUZO?

EXCUSE ME, SIR!

ARGH!

SO ANNOYING!

Ignoring me again!

WHAT-EVER.

JUST SEND HIM ON HIS WAY.

THE CLERK AGAIN?

22

24

26

TAYU...

IT IS THE DUTY OF *TAYU* TO ONLY THINK OF HER MASTER AS SHE GOES TO HIM.

WHAT?

BE-CAUSE...

I HAVE NO OTHER TALENTS.

IT IS CUSTOMARY TO PROCEED WITHOUT A MOMENT OF DISTRACTION.

I'M EMBAR-RASSED TO SAY, BUT I AM A NEWCOMER WITH LESS THAN A YEAR SINCE ENTERING YURI.

SINCE I AM A *TAYU* WITHOUT MUCH TALENT FOR DANCE OR MUSIC...*

THE LEAST I CAN DO IS TRY MY BEST TO BE THE MOST DEVOTED ON THE WAY TO MY MASTER'S.

WHAT YOU WIT-NESSED WAS MY PALTRY SENSE OF PRIDE.

HEH

I SEE...

STILL, I WOULD RATHER DIE THAN STRAY FROM MY PRINCIPLES.

*Some *tayu* refused dance and music for fear of being likened to a common entertainer. Others were genuinely still green.

28

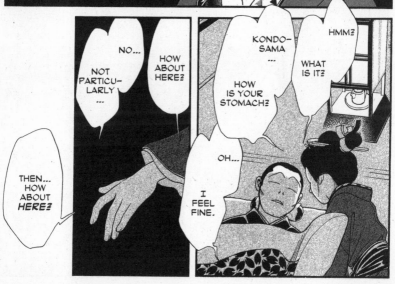

GA AH !!

MI...Z!

PLEASE
RELAX...

THIS IS
JUST A
REMEDY.

NO...

BUT...

MI...Z!

ACK...

WELL...

KEEPING WATCH JUST IN CASE.

SHALL
WE
PATROL
THE
TOWN?

Y-YES!
I THINK
THAT'S
A FINE
IDEA!

30

NOW THAT YOU MENTION IT...

I WONDER IF HE COMES FROM A LARGE STORE IN EDO THAT DECIDED TO OPEN A STOREFRONT HERE?

DID YOU NOTICE HE HAD AN EDO ACCENT?

AND THAT MAN WORKING FOR HIM...

IT WAS AS IF HE WAS A FIREMAN'S AID...

I STILL CAN'T BELIEVE WHAT AN ODD CHARACTER HE WAS.

UKINOSUKE-SAN, THAT IS...

I'M SORRY. I DON'T EVEN WANT TO TALK ABOUT IT.

A FIREMAN?

...

HM?

DID YOU SAY SOMETHING, OKITA SENSEI?

IT CAN'T BE...

WITH A SUBTLE SENSE OF SUSPICION...

THE NEXT DAY...

THE THREE RETURNED TO KYOTO BY BOAT.

PLEASE...

COME BACK AGAIN.

SIGH

HOW PRETTY WAS MIYUKI-DAYU?

BLUSH

IT'S NOT CUSTOMARY FOR YUJO OF OSAKA TO SEE THEIR CLIENTS OFF, NO MATTER HOW IMPORTANT THEY ARE.

AND YET SHE CAME ALL THE WAY TO FUNABA.

YOU ARE A MAN OF GREAT FORTUNE, CAPTAIN!

IN KYOTO, WHILE STRUGGLING WITH THE IMPERIAL COURT MANAGEMENT OF PARTIES FRIENDLY TO THE CHOSHU CLAN...

SHOGUN TOKUGAWA IEMOCHI WAS SUCCESSFUL IN OBTAINING FROM EMPEROR KOMEI AN IMPERIAL SANCTION FOR A PUNITIVE EXPEDITION AGAINST THE CHOSHU.

CONGRATULATIONS, MY LORD.

I AM GRATEFUL FOR THAT, HIGO.

YES. I KNOW YOU'VE WORKED HARD.

JAPAN CAN FINALLY UNITE IF WE ARE ABLE TO DEFEAT THE CHOSHU ...

...AND THE BAKUFU CAN FINALLY FOCUS ON DIPLOMATIC ISSUES WITH FOREIGN FORCES— OUR *TRUE* ENEMY.

WHAT...?!

WSS WSS WSS ...

THIS IS A DELIBERATE AFFRONT TO ME!

THAT ROTTEN #@&% !!

MY LORD! BE CALM, PLEASE!

This is a shōjo manga...

HE DRIVES ME INTO A CORNER AND THEN WAITS FOR ME TO COME BEGGING!

HE'S MADE IT HIS LIFE'S WORK TO REMIND ME OF HIS SUPERIORITY!

...AND HE CANNOT BEAR THE FACT THAT I WAS CHOSEN DESPITE BEING NINE YEARS HIS JUNIOR.

EIGHT YEARS AGO, WE FOUND OURSELVES WITH THE MISFORTUNE OF HAVING TO FIGHT FOR THE SEAT OF SHOGUN...

PERHAPS HITOTSUBASHI-KO IS WAITING FOR *YOUR* SUMMONS?

WITH YOUR PERMIS-SION, MY LORD...

HIGO...

I SEE...

HE *STILL* HAS NOT COME TO THE CASTLE DESPITE BEING REPEATEDLY SUMMONED BY THE COUNSELORS...

THAT IS THE KIND OF *BITTER MAN* HITOTSUBASHI YOSHINOBU IS!

YOU MAY NOT BE THERE NOW, BUT THE OSAKA CASTLE IS YOUR RESIDENCE.

HE IS LIKELY WAITING FOR A DIRECT SUMMONS FROM YOU SO THAT HE CAN SERVE YOU WHOLE-HEARTEDLY.

HE IS PROBABLY VERY MUCH AWARE THAT YOU DO NOT THINK OF HIM FONDLY.

COULD THAT REALLY...

...BE HIS REASON?

37

HOW PURE AND ADORABLE THIS MAN IS.

PERHAPS MY THOUGHTS CAUSED HITOTSUBASHI TO ACT SO PERVERSELY.

I APPRE-CIATE YOUR INSIGHT, HIGO.

I SEE...

IT IS EASY TO THINK OF THE WORLD AS EVIL.

THUD

WHEW

THE 14TH SHOGUN, TOKUGAWA IEMOCHI, WAS JUST BARELY 20 YEARS OLD.

THIS CHARAC-TER...

...INCLUDING THE EASE WITH WHICH HE COULD BE PERSUADED, MADE HIM SO LOVABLE TO THOSE WHO SERVED HIM.

HE WAS SHUNNED BY THOSE AROUND HIM AS IMPOSSIBLE TO UNDER-STAND.

ON THE OTHER HAND

...HITOTSU-BASHI YOSHINOBU WAS KNOWN FOR HIS QUICK WIT AND HIS IMMUNITY TO PERSUASION.

39

TWELVE YEARS AFTER PERRY'S ARRIVAL IN URAGA...

THE FOUR-NATION COALITION REPRESENTING ENGLAND, THE U.S., FRANCE AND THE NETHERLANDS HAD ARRIVED OFFSHORE IN HYOGO, CHASING THE SHOGUN IEMOCHI WHO HAD BEEN OCCUPYING OSAKA.

THEY WERE ONCE AGAIN APPLYING PRESSURE ON THE BAKUFU TO ACCEPT THEIR REQUEST FOR AN OFFICIAL, IMPERIALLY SANCTIONED TRADE TREATY AND THE IMMEDIATE OPENING OF THE HYOGO PORT, WHICH WAS CENTRAL TO JAPAN AT THE TIME.

SEP- TEMBER 22 OF THE FIRST YEAR OF KEIO (NOVEM- BER 10, 1865).

EVE- NING...

KONDO, OKITA AND SEIZABURO HAD JUST RETURNED TO KYOTO FROM OSAKA REGARDING THIS MATTER.

"RO" 3
ROKU AREBA KU ARI
"ALLOWANCE COMES AT A PRICE"
Submitted by Hiroki from Kanagawa

KAZE HIKARU IROHA KARUTA

PLEASE DON'T GET UP, SIR!

I WAS SO CONCERNED WHEN I HEARD YOU'D FALLEN ILL!

OH...

I'M SORRY FOR MY PATHETIC STATE, KONDO...

THEY WENT STRAIGHT TO THE PROTECTOR OF KYOTO AND THE MASTER OF THE SHINSENGUMI, LORD MATSUDAIRA KATAMORI OF HIGO.

WHAT?!

HIGO-SAMA?!

I WAS FINALLY ABLE TO OBTAIN IMPERIAL SANCTION FOR DEFEATING THE CHOSHU...

IT'S NOT SO SERIOUS.

THE RELIEF MUST HAVE MADE ME DIZZY.

MY LORD!

YOUR HEALTH IS A PRIORITY!

41

I APPRECIATE YOUR CONCERN, BUT IT'S NOT NECESSARY.

TELL ME. HOW IS THE SITUATION IN OSAKA?

I HAVE BEEN CONSTANTLY CONCERNED OVER YOUR HEALTH.

MY LORD, YOU'VE BEEN ASKED TO DO TASKS OF SUCH GRAVE RESPONSIBILITY WHEN YOU WERE NOT WELL TO BEGIN WITH...

EVEN AT THE CASTLE, THE MEN ARE FATIGUED FROM THE STRING OF MEETINGS, AND THE ATMOSPHERE IS SOMBER.

YES ...

THE PEOPLE FEAR THE BLACK SHIPS.

IS IT TRUE THAT HE HAS YET TO ARRIVE AT THE CASTLE?

WHAT RUMORS?

WHAT CONCERNED ME MOST WERE THE RUMORS GOING AROUND TOWN ABOUT HITOTSU-BASHI-KO.

I SEE ...

IT'S AS I FEARED.

AT LEAST THOSE REASONS ARE PLAUSIBLE...

IT'S A BLESSING IN DISGUISE.

THE REASON IS RUMORED TO BE ANYTHING FROM A SECRET AILMENT TO AN ANTI-BAKUFU PLOT.

WHAT DO YOU MEAN?

HITOTSU-BASHI-KO'S DISAPPEAR-ANCE...

...IS NOT A RARE OCCUR-RENCE.

WHAT?

I'VE BEEN THINKING ABOUT UKINOSUKE-SAN.

KAMIYA-SAN...

43

...AT LEAST "HIGO-SAMA," WOULDN'T HE?

A MERCHANT WOULD CALL HIM "AIZU-SAMA" OR...

I JUST REMEMBERED THOUGH...

HE CALLED KATAMORI-SAMA, "HIGO."

WHAT USE IS IT DWELLING ON THE MAN'S COMPLETE LACK OF MANNERS?!

THE MAN'S ATTITUDE TOWARD *BUSHI* IS ABNORMAL TO BEGIN WITH!

WELL...

I SUPPOSE IT'S OF NO USE...

I DIDN'T WANT TO USE THE *BUSHI* CARD, SO I LEFT MY *KATANA*. WHAT A HUGE MISTAKE THAT WAS!

SOJI, KAMIYA-KUN.

SORRY TO KEEP YOU WAITING.

DON'T YOU THINK YOUR LANGUAGE HAS GOTTEN A LITTLE TOO... STRONG RECENTLY?

KAMIYA-SAN...

I SHOULD HAVE *KILLED* HIM FOR BEING SO RUDE, THAT ROTTEN ...!!

HE SAID HE WAS MERELY FEELING LIGHT-HEADED...

...BUT HE COULDN'T HIDE HOW TIRED HE WAS.

CAP-TAIN!

HOW WAS KATA-MORI-SAMA?!

WE MUST PREPARE SO THAT THE SHINSENGUMI IS READY TO DEPLOY AS HIS SUBSTITUTE.

HE WILL LIKELY BE RESTING FOR THE NEXT TWO TO THREE DAYS.

HE DECIDED NOT TO ACCOMPANY THE SHOGUN TO OSAKA TOMOR-ROW.

YES?

THE RUMOR YOU HEARD ABOUT HITOTSU-BASHI-KO GOING MISSING...

IT APPEARS TO BE *TRUE.*

YES, SIR!

OH, AND SOJI.

CHIEF SHIN-MON WAS ...

...SOME-ONE HITOTSU-BASHI-KO CALLED TO KYOTO, WASN'T IT?

WE'RE TALKING ABOUT SHINMON TATSU-GORO.

YOU'VE BEEN IN KYOTO SO LONG YOU PROBABLY DON'T KNOW.

OH RIGHT.

CHIEF SHIN-MON?

HE'S DEFINITELY NOT A DISCREET MAN.

SO THEY HAD A TOTAL OF 300 MEN WORK AS HITOTSU-BASHI-KO'S PERSONAL SECURITY WHEN THEY CAME TO KYOTO.

RIGHT! HE WANTED HIS DAUGH-TER TO BE HIS MIS-TRESS.

HE'S QUITE A CELEBRITY IN EDO.

THE FAMILY HEAD OF ONE OF THE THREE TOKUGAWA FAMILIES ...

...HAS A DAUGHTER OF THE FIRE BRIGADE AS HIS *MISTRESS*?!

HE'S THE HEAD OF THE "O CLAN," THE FIRE BRIGADE IN ASAKUSA.

WELL ...

I THINK MAYBE ...

NOT THAT MY OPINION MATTERS ...

WHAT KIND OF **MAN** IS HE?!

I CAN'T **BE-LIEVE** IT!

FOUR DAYS LATER ...

ON THE DAWN OF THE DEADLINE TO PROVIDE THE FOUR-NATION COALITION WITH AN ANSWER...

OPEN THE GATE!

COMMANDER OF THE IMPERIAL PALACE DEFENSE AND NAVAL DEFENSE, HITOTSU-BASHI YOSHI-NOBU ...

...HAS ARRIVED BY REQUEST OF THE SHOGUN!

50

53

*Not under the official Tokugawa umbrella, but a clan that joined after the Battle of Sekigahara that includes Satsuma, Choshu and Tosa.

I ONLY HOPE IT WILL GO SO SMOOTHLY.

YOU THINK YOU WOULD BE MORE PERSUASIVE THAN THE SHOGUN?

HA HA HA

IN OTHER WORDS, YOU'RE PRETTY MUCH FAMILY WITH THE EMPEROR.

IF MEMORY SERVES, YOUR MOTHER WAS FROM THE ARISUGA-WANO MIYAKE FAMILY.*

BESIDES ...

IF HIS MEMORY OF THE BAKUFU ITSELF IS TAINTED, MY EFFORTS WILL BE WORTH NOTHING.

THERE ARE MANY ANTI-BAKUFU NOBLES WHO SERVE THE EMPEROR.

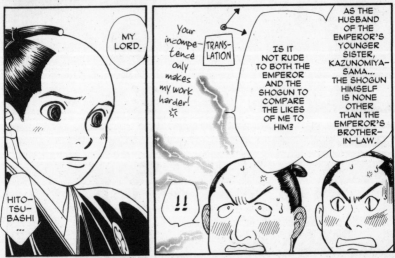

MY LORD.

HITO-TSU-BASHI ...

Your incompe-tence only makes my work harder!

TRANS-LATION

IS IT NOT RUDE TO BOTH THE EMPEROR AND THE SHOGUN TO COMPARE THE LIKES OF ME TO HIM?

AS THE HUSBAND OF THE EMPEROR'S YOUNGER SISTER, KAZUNOMIYA-SAMA... THE SHOGUN HIMSELF IS NONE OTHER THAN THE EMPEROR'S BROTHER-IN-LAW.

*One of the four imperially sanctioned families.

54

YOU'LL SEE.

THE THREE TOKUGAWA FAMILIES* EXIST TO SUPPORT THE SHOGUNATE.

TRUST ME, WOULD YA?

YOU JUST HAVE TO START WITH GETTING AN EXTENSION!

HMPH

Your attitude toward the shogun is unacceptable!

BUNGO-DONO! IZU-DONO!

WHO WILL YOU SEND TO HYOGO?

I WANT TO SPEAK TO HIM OF A PLAN!

...THERE WAS NEVER ANY BAD BLOOD BETWEEN IEMOCHI AND YOSHINOBU ON A PERSONAL LEVEL.

....

ALTHOUGH THEY HAD FORMERLY FOUGHT OVER THE SHOGUN SEAT...

55   *The Tayasu, Hitotsubashi and Shimizu families were not independent clans but were considered part of the Shogun family

HOWEVER, IEMOCHI, WHO HAD WON THIS CONTEST BASED ON FAMILY RANKING, HARBORED AN INFERIORITY COMPLEX TOWARD YOSHINBOU...

IT WAS NOT THESE MEN WHO HAD VIED FOR THE POSITION.

THEY WERE MERELY RECRUITED AS POLITICAL TOOLS BY THEIR RESPECTIVE FACTIONS.

...WHO HAD ALWAYS BEEN PRAISED FOR HIS WIT AND INTELLECT.

IEMOCHI'S COLD ATTITUDE TOWARD YOSHINOBU WAS A FACTOR THAT LED TO THEIR UNFORTUNATE FATES.

MY LORD!

THEY AGREED TO AN EXTENSION OF *TEN DAYS!*

IS THAT TRUE?!

GOOD WORK!

YES! I DID JUST AS HITOTSU-BASHI-KO ADVISED!

56

SHMP

HITOTSU-
BASHI ...

HE
TRULY
IS A
GREAT
MAN.

...

HE WAS
PROBABLY
THINKING
ABOUT
THIS MATTER
FOR THE
PAST TEN
DAYS!

THAT'S
NON-
SENSE,
MY
LORD!

HE WAS
ABLE TO DO
IN A DAY
WHAT WE
COULD
NOT IN
TEN.

PUTTING
ON A
SHOW LIKE
THAT!

THIS IS
JUST HIS
SIGNATURE
MOVE!

62

SHUT UP!

C'MON.

HOW DO YOU EXPECT ME TO *NOT* DRINK ?!

YOU'VE HAD ENOUGH TO DRINK.

I'M NOT SURE IF YOU RIDE WAVES TO OBTAIN IMPERIAL SANCTIONS ...

DON'T YOU THINK HE CAN RIDE THIS WAVE AND OBTAIN AN IMPERIAL SANCTION?

SLAM

?!

ALL OF THEM!

I'M SUR-ROUNDED BY...

...IDIOTS!

UKINO-SUKE-SAN?!

HEY?!

OH, I KNOW.

YOU'RE JUST TRYING TO CHEER ME UP.

I APPRECIATE IT, BUNGO. IZU...

TH-THAT'S NOT AT ALL WHAT WE'RE TRYING TO IMPLY!

GAH!

Ha

DO YOU NOT WANT TO OBTAIN IMPERIAL SANCTION?

LET US EAGERLY AWAIT HIS SOMBER RETURN.

BUT I DOUBT HE WILL BE ABLE TO OBTAIN IMPERIAL SANCTION JUST AS EASILY.

THANK YOU FOR EVERY-THING.

I WANT YOU TO GET A GOOD NIGHT'S REST TONIGHT.

YOU ALL MUST BE TIRED.

TEARS

YES, MY LORD!

IN MORE MODERN TERMS ...

...IEMOCHI WOULD LIKELY BE REFERRED TO AS A SOFTY.

63

UKINOSUKE-SAN?

I WONDER WHY...

DIDN'T YOU GET THE FEELING THAT UKI-SAN WAS GENUINELY DEPRESSED JUST NOW?

YES...

THAT WOMAN WAS SPEAKING IN AN EDO DIALECT TOO.

HE'S NOT FROM OSAKA, IS HE?

WHO THE HECK IS THAT GUY?!

I WONDER IF UKI-SAN'S ACTUALLY A REALLY BAD GUY?

THAT PRETTY LADY GETTING ALL FLUSTERED AFTER HEARING "SHINSEN-GUMI" IS A LITTLE SUSPICIOUS.

64

I WAS HEADED TO KATAMORI-SAMA'S JUST NOW TO GET THE DETAILS.

IT'S GOTTEN AROUND ALREADY?!

HITOTSU-BASHI-KO...

IS EVERY-THING OKAY WITH HIM?

I WAS JUST IN TOWN AND...

SOJI.

IS EVERY-THING ALL RIGHT?

SO...

WHAT'S ...

WHAT?!

THE COUNSELORS, LORD ABE OF BUNGO AND LORD MATSUMAE OF IZU, WERE DISMISSED.

APPARENTLY, IT WAS A RARE DIRECT ORDER FROM THE IMPERIAL COURT...

IT'S FOR THEIR DECISION TO APPROVE THE OPENING OF HYOGO BY THE BAKUFU ALONE.

BUT... I THOUGHT THEY GOT THE DEADLINE EXTENDED TEN DAYS...

THAT WAS HITOTSU-BASHI-KO'S DOING, REMEMBER?

UNFORTUNATELY, THE COUNSELORS HAD ALREADY REPORTED THE DECISION TO OPEN THE PORT BEFORE HE'D ARRIVED AT OSAKA CASTLE.

NEWS OF THE EXTENSION DID TAKE CARE OF SOME OF THE CONFUSION IN THE IMPERIAL COURT.

HOWEVER, THE IMPERIAL COURT DOESN'T HAVE JURISDICTION OVER HUMAN AFFAIRS IN THE BAKUFU.

BUT THE BACKLASH TOWARD THE BAKUFU WAS APPARENTLY QUITE SIGNIFICANT.

AND YET THEY PUSHED IT...

...THEY KNOW WHO'S PULLING THE STRINGS FROM THE SHADOWS.

IT SEEMS...

JUST TELL ME NEXT TIME IF YOU DON'T WANT ME AROUND.

OTHER-WISE...

I'VE VOWED TO ALWAYS FOLLOW YOU.

THANKS.

HUH?!

IT MAKES ME HAPPY...

...TO THINK THAT SOMEONE CARES.

I HOPE...

...KONDO SENSEI APPRECIATES ME THE SAME WAY.

KATAMORI-SAMA AND THE SHOGUN...

THEY ALL APPRECIATE KONDO SENSEI AND THE SHINSENGUMI, DON'T YOU THINK?

WHEN VIEWED IN RETROSPECT...

EVEN GREAT HISTORICAL EVENTS ARE MERELY A SERIES OF DAILY EPISODES FOR THOSE WHO LIVED IT.

WHY IS IT THAT...

...ONLY THE SHOGUN AND HITOTSU-BASHI-KO ARE UNABLE TO APPRECIATE EACH OTHER?

THERE ARE TOO MANY PEOPLE WHO CAN RECOGNIZE YOU IN KYOTO. HOW MANY TIMES HAVE I TOLD YOU TO QUIT PLAYING MERCHANT HERE?!

MY GOOD-NESS!

MY HEAD'S THROB-BING...

THE SPLIT IN THE TOKU-GAWA BAKUFU...

...HAD BEGUN TO SLOWLY DEEPEN.

73

SEP-
TEMBER
30 OF
THE FIRST
YEAR
OF KEIO
(NO-
VEMBER
17, 1865).

THE
NEWS
WAS
BROKEN
AT THE
OSAKA
CASTLE.

ABE
BUNGO AND
MATSUMAE
IZU ARE
DISMISSED
?!

WHAT RIGHT
DOES THE
IMPERIAL
COURT HAVE
TO MEDDLE
IN SUCH
MATTERS?!

THEIR
ATTITUDE IS
COMPLETELY
*UNACCEPT-
ABLE!*

THEY
ARE
ORDERED
TO BE
STRIPPED
OF THEIR
OFFICIAL
TITLES
AND
RESTRICTED
TO THEIR
HOME-
TOWNS.

YES.

IT WAS
DETERMINED
THAT
DECIDING
TO OPEN THE
HYOGO PORT
ON THEIR
OWN WAS
UNSCRUPU-
LOUS.

"HA" は ♥

HANA YORI
KYOKUCHO

"CAPTAIN OVER GIRLS"

Submitted by
Tsukimi-san
from Nagasaki

KAZE
HIKARU
IROHA
KARUTA

75

76

"UNLIKE ME, HE'S VERY TALENTED AND QUITE FAMILIAR WITH THE EMPEROR, SO I'M SURE THAT YOU'LL BE QUITE PLEASED WITH HIM!"

"I NOMINATE HITOTSU-BASHI YOSHINOBU TO THE SHOGUNATE!"

BLEH

CAN YOU BELIEVE IT?!

DO YOU KNOW WHAT HE WROTE IN HIS LETTER OF RESIGNATION, HIGO?

IT'S NO USE!

WHY DON'T YOU TELL THIS TO THE SHOGUN?

I CAN'T DEAL WITH SUCH A WARPED MIND.

THAT'S A GRAVE OVERSIMPLIFICATION, DON'T YOU THINK?

BESIDES...

Who's the warped one?

I CAN SEE HOW IEMOCHI WOULD TAKE IT THE WRONG WAY...

...WHEN THOSE MEN ARE DISMISSED WITHOUT WARNING LIKE THAT.

THEY MAY BE IDIOTS...

...BUT THOSE MEN SERIOUSLY THINK THEY ARE PROTECTING IEMOCHI.

77

HITOTSU-
BASHI-
DONO...!

I KNOW...
I'M A
GOOD GUY,
RIGHT?

THE WORLD IS
NOT GOING TO
CHANGE JUST
BECAUSE A
CONTEMPTUOUS
MAN LOSES
HIS COOL.

WELL
...

I
DON'T
KNOW
ABOUT
THAT...

ALL
I CAN
DO IS...

...ENJOY
THE
RIDE.

A MAN OF ULTIMATE INSIGHT AND UNADULTERATED CURIOSITY.

...IF HE'S BEING OPTIMISTIC OR JUST SUPPRESSING HIS DISAPPOINTMENT.

I HAVE NO IDEA...

IF ONE WERE TO EVALUATE YOSHINOBU...

...ONE WOULD LIKELY DESCRIBE HIM AS A MAN OF THESE PRIMARY CHARACTERISTICS.

BUT THAT IS BESIDE THE POINT.

THE SITUATION DEMANDS OUR ATTENTION.

THANKS FOR ABIDING MY *REQUEST*, HIGO!

I'M GOING HOME.

SORRY FOR STAYING SO LONG.

...

WHAT ?!

THE SHOGUN'S SUBMITTED A LETTER OF RESIGNATION TO THE EMPEROR AND IS RETURNING TO EDO?!

HOW RIDICULOUS IS *THAT?!*

HE MUST BE *REALLY* UPSET...

...ABOUT THAT WHOLE COUNCIL DISMISSAL INCIDENT.

I THINK IT'S JUST THE WAKE-UP CALL THAT THE IMPERIAL COURT NEEDS!

ALL THEY DO IS COMPLAIN AND FAIL TO REALIZE THAT WITHOUT THE BAKUFU, NO POLITICAL MATTER WOULD EVER BE RESOLVED!

FROM THE MATSUMAE CLAN

WE ONLY HAVE *FOUR DAYS* UNTIL WE HAVE TO GIVE AN ANSWER TO THE FOREIGN COALITION!

BUT...

THIS IS NO TIME FOR THE IMPERIAL COURT AND THE BAKUFU TO BE *FEUDING!*

I THINK YOU SAID THAT ONE TOO MANY TIMES.

"To be," that is...

OKITA-SAN.

KAMIYA.

80

81

ISN'T IT *OBVIOUS?*

WE'RE GOING TO *STOP* THE SHOGUN!

UMM... ME TOO? REALLY?

WHAT'S GOING ON IN FUSHIMI?

I DIDN'T DO ANYTHING!

I DON'T KNOW WHY YOU TWO WERE SPECIFIED TO COME WITH ME...

DO YOU?

THE GREAT KATAMORI-SAMA IS SO DESERVING OF HIS RECOGNITION!

WHAT SOUND JUDGMENT!

OH *GOOD!*

IN ANY CASE, THOSE ARE THE ORDERS! WE'VE NO CHOICE BUT TO FOLLOW THEM!

HOW WOULD I KNOW ?!

Why aren't I going?!

AREN'T THERE MORE RELIABLE MEN FOR SECURITY?

BUT WHY IN THE WORLD AM I GOING?

...I AM SO GRATEFUL FOR THE HONOR...

...TO BE ABLE TO SERVE LIKE THIS.

EVEN IF IT COSTS MY LIFE...

I'M GOING TO STOP THE SHOGUN!

AND SO AT MIDNIGHT ON THE THIRD... KONDO AND HIS TWO MEN ACCOMPANIED MATSUDAIRA KATAMORI AND HEADED TO FUSHIMI.

EVEN IF THIS ASSIGNMENT WAS SOME MISTAKE...

...?

THUP

WAS THAT...

WAS THAT THE SHOGUN?!

!

SUCH A YOUNG VOICE...

...FROM THE SHOGUN I SERVE!

SENSEI ...!

UR ...

URR...

KONDO'S TEARS WERE UNDER-STANDABLE...

I HAVE NOT COME TO SAY FAREWELL.

FOR KONDO, WHO CAME FROM FARMING ROOTS, IT WAS BUT A DREAM TO BE ABLE TO HEAR THE SHOGUN.

ALTHOUGH HE WAS AN OFFICIAL *BUSHI*, MEN UNDER A CERTAIN RANKING WERE NOT EVEN PERMITTED TO LOOK AT THE SHOGUN.

THE EMPEROR HAS REFUSED YOUR RESIGNATION.

IN HIS WORDS, "IT IS UNACCEPTABLE."

IF YOU IGNORE THIS AND RETURN TO EDO...

...YOU WILL CAUSE A *SCHISM* BETWEEN THE BAKUFU AND THE IMPERIAL COURT!

I BEG YOU TO WITHDRAW YOUR RESIGNATION AND RETURN TO KYOTO.

PLEASE REROUTE YOUR PARTY TO THE NIJO CASTLE!

THE BAKUFU AND IMPERIAL COURT WILL NOT SPLIT...

THAT IS *NOT TRUE!*

HIGO...

...SO LONG AS HITOTSU-BASHI YOSHI-NOBU IS AROUND.

I AM AN UNNECESSARY PLAYER.

92

93

CLA

WHAT ARE YOU ALL LOOKING AT?!

IT IS COMPLETELY UNACCEPTABLE FOR A RONIN TO BE SPEAKING TO THE SHOGUN LIKE THIS!

I CANNOT BURDEN YOU WITH SUCH A TASK!

I AM OKITA SOJI, CAPTAIN OF THE FIRST TROOP OF THE SHINSENGUMI!

96

I BELIEVE YOU'RE PART OF THIS PARTY.

PLEASE COME OUT AND EXPLAIN!

FORMER COUNSELORS, ABE AND MATSUMAE!

WHAT?! THIS IS HITOTSUBASHI YOSHINOBU?!

YES, SIR!

...

DO YOU REALIZE THAT THE EXISTENCE OF JAPAN IS AT STAKE?! WHAT WERE YOU THINKING?!

YOU'RE BEHIND ALL THIS RESIGNATION MADNESS, AREN'T YOU?!

100

101

102

REMEM-
BER
MEETING
ME?

IN
SHIN-
MACHI?

YOU
KNEW
WHO I
WAS
FROM
THE
BEGIN-
NING,
DIDN'T
YOU?

I
HAVE
NO IDEA
WHAT
YOU
MEAN,
SIR.

You
may look
up.

THERE
IS NO WAY
I WOULD
HAVE EVER
SEEN YOU
IN A YURI.

WHAT
DO YOU
HAVE UP
YOUR SLEEVE
THAT YOU
WANT ME
TO BE
INDEBTED
TO YOU
FOR?

YOU
POOR
FELLOW.

Ha.

I STILL
HAVE NO
IDEA.

...I'M LEFT WITH **NO CHOICE** BUT TO COMMIT *SEPPUKU!*

IF YOU STILL DO NOT PERMIT IT...

IN THE END...

AND THEY PUSHED FOR THE IMPERIAL SANCTION OF THE TRADE TREATY AS THE CONSENSUS AMONG ALL CLANS.

SEKISHIRO NIJO NARIYUKI

AND SO...

EDO FIRE BRIGADE

AND IN SUCH A SITUATION, BECAUSE THE MEN UNDER ME ARE HOT-BLOODED...

...BE PREPARED FOR RETALIATION!

IT WAS UNDER SUCH A THREAT THAT HE WAS ABLE TO OBTAIN IMPERIAL SANCTION (HEH).

H-HITOTSU-BASHI-DONO, WAIT!

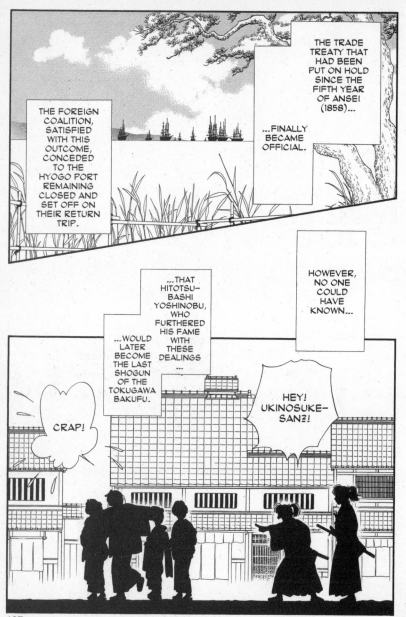

THE TRADE TREATY THAT HAD BEEN PUT ON HOLD SINCE THE FIFTH YEAR OF ANSEI (1858)...

...FINALLY BECAME OFFICIAL.

THE FOREIGN COALITION, SATISFIED WITH THIS OUTCOME, CONCEDED TO THE HYOGO PORT REMAINING CLOSED AND SET OFF ON THEIR RETURN TRIP.

HOWEVER, NO ONE COULD HAVE KNOWN...

...THAT HITOTSU-BASHI YOSHINOBU, WHO FURTHERED HIS FAME WITH THESE DEALINGS...

...WOULD LATER BECOME THE LAST SHOGUN OF THE TOKUGAWA BAKUFU.

CRAP!

HEY! UKINOSUKE-SAN?!

"Literally, "young teacher."

*Soji's childhood name.

110

111

"PLEASE RUN ME OVER AS YOU PASS THROUGH!"

HIS FAVORITES LIST HASN'T CHANGED A JOT SINCE HE WAS 9 YEARS OLD.

OH WELL.

WHO DOESN'T LOVE THE CAPTAIN?

I CAN'T THINK OF ANOTHER MAN WHO COULD PERFORM LIKE THAT...

...SUR-ROUNDED BY ARMED MEN AND IN FRONT OF THE SHOGUN.

THE CAPTAIN'S HEART AND SOUL...

...WAS PROBABLY THE KEY TO MOVING THE SHOGUN.

I REFUSE TO ADMIT IT WAS THE DOINGS OF *THAT* MAN!

IT INFURIATES ME TO EVEN RECALL HIM!

GAH!

WHAT THE HECK, KAMIYA?!

112

FOR THE DUTY OF INSPECTING THE CHOSHU THAT EVERYBODY TRIED TO AVOID?!

HA HA HA!

KONDO CAME FORTH AND ASKED?!

← Nagai-san and others only go to Hiroshima, because it's dangerous (heh)

THE KIND THAT CARRIES OUT HIS DUTY WITH HIS LIFE. THE BAKUFU LACKS THAT KIND OF BLIND LOYALTY.

THAT'S THE KIND OF MAN YOU WANT ON YOUR SIDE.

HOW INTERESTING, HIGO. YOU SHOULD LET HIM DO IT.

AND SO...

THE NAME OF KONDO ISAMI HAD BEGUN TO DRAW INTEREST SINCE THE SHOGUN'S "RETURN TO EDO" MISHAP.

HITOTSU-BASHI-DONO...

(And so irresponsible!)

You're so easily amused

THEREFORE, THE SHINSENGUMI WERE TO SEND EIGHT MEN INCLUDING KONDO.

NO!

I'M NOT CONVINCED!

114

115

116

117

IT'S LIKELY THAT ANYTHING WEST OF HIROSHIMA WILL REQUIRE GREAT SECRECY.

I'M PUTTING THE SPY, YAMAZAKI SUSUMU, AS THE CAPTAIN'S SECURITY.

HE'S ABLE AND SMART.

YAMAZAKI CAN BETTER SERVE THE CAPTAIN THAN YOU AND YOUR FOOLISH HONESTY.

THIS DISCUSSION IS OVER.

...!

SLAM!

SOJI!

THIS IS WHAT MUST BE DONE.

THANKS.

THAT LITTLE...!

TOSHI...

...

"DON'T BE SUCH A CHILD, SOJI!"

"CAN YOU NOT UNDERSTAND WHY I WANT YOU TO STAND ON YOUR OWN TWO FEET?!"

121

122

I'LL WAIT FOR YOU AT THE DOJO.

YES...

...HE WOULD CRY ALONE.

I THOUGHT...

I'M SORRY TO KEEP YOU WAITING.

HE HAD ALREADY REGAINED HIS CALM.

AND HIS EYES WERE DRY...

YET...

...WHEN HE ARRIVED AT THE DOJO, HE WAS NO MORE THAN TEN STEPS BEHIND ME.

HE AMAZES ME.

HE'S FRUSTRATED ENOUGH TO GET SICK...

GOOD WORK.

TH- THANK YOU VERY MUCH...

ONLY PRACTICE WAS TWICE AS HARD.

FWOMP

TRUE *BUSHI* ARE STRONG TO THE CORE.

"SHH! SOJIRO! YOU'RE ALREADY AWAKE?"

126

WHAT A STRANGE DREAM...

OKITA SENSEI'S EYES WERE FIXATED...

HE'S SOMEONE SOJI'S ALWAYS FOLLOWED AND ADORED.

I WOULD RATHER DIE...

THIS MUST BE SO HARD. I'M SURE THE CAPTAIN HAS HIS REASONS, BUT...

OKITA SENSEI!?!

IT'S ICE-COLD!

HOW LONG HAVE YOU BEEN GONE ?!

WHAT
IS IT?

GO
BACK.

OH...!

HE CUTS THROUGH EACH FALLING LEAF...

ONE BY ONE...

EVERY LEAF THAT FALLS...

...AS IF IT'S A CEREMONY TO HOLD BACK HIS TEARS.

IN THIS DARKNESS...

I MAY HURT YOU UNINTENTIONALLY.

THIS MAN WITH HIS DRY EYES...

...IN THE COLD DARKNESS OF SHATTERED HOPE...

IT'S AS IF I...

MUST I REPEAT MYSELF, KAMIYA-SAN?!

130

IT'S MY WILL.

I WROTE IT TO HIKOGORO-SAN* AND HIS FAMILY IN HINO.

THIS LETTER...

IT WOULD BE DIFFERENT IF HE WERE OFFICIALLY MY ADOPTED SON.

BUT THERE ARE OTHER MEN WHO COULD CLAIM THE INHERITANCE OF THE *TEN'NEN RISHIN RYU.*

NO— IT'S NOT RIGHT.

NOBODY WOULD COMPLAIN!

ABOUT YOU.

AND ABOUT SOJI.

I'VE WRITTEN DOWN EVERYTHING YOU SHOULD NEED.

SEND IT THERE AFTER YOU PERSONALLY CONFIRM.

KONDO-SAN...

*A student of the *Ten'nen Rishin ryu* and the Shinsengumi supporter. Kondo's stepbrother and Hijikata's older sister's husband.

134

I KNOW.

DON'T YOU DIE.

...

GRIP

!

WOOPS

HERE, SENSEI.

A NEW RIDING GLOVE AND LEGGINGS.

YOU'RE GOING TO CHASE AFTER HIM IN SECRET, RIGHT?

DON'T WORRY. I'LL TAKE CARE OF EVERYTHING HERE.

KAMIYA-SAN...!

I DECIDED TO ASK HIM ONCE AGAIN.

THAT WAS MY PLAN, BUT...

I WOULD BE CONFUSING THE NATURAL ORDER OF THINGS...

...TO JUST THROW A FIT, SAYING I WANT TO GO WITH HIM WITHOUT REFLECTING ON MY OWN SHORTCOMINGS.

IF SENSEI SINCERELY TELLS ME NOT TO COME...

IF I AM ABLE TO SEE THAT...

I MUST CONSIDER NOT GOING AS A WAY TO SERVE HIM.

BE-CAUSE...

...I AM BUSHI.

OH, CAPTAIN KONDO!

HIJI-KATA-SAN?

THE VICE CAPTAIN IS CALLING FOR YOU IN THE INNER COURT.

OKITA SENSEI!

SENSEI IS A TRUE *BUSHI* AND TWICE THE MAN OF ANY OTHER SOLDIER!

PLEASE TAKE OKITA SENSEI WITH YOU!

IT'S JUST WHAT YOU HOPED FOR!

IF YOU CAN CONVINCE THE VICE CAPTAIN, IT'S JUST AS GOOD AS CONVINCING THE CAPTAIN HIMSELF!

I'M ROOTING FOR YOU, OKITA SENSEI!

AND IF...

...LIKE OUR NORMAL RELATION-SHIP HAS BEEN REVERSED?

WHY DO I FEEL...

I CAN FOLLOW HIM WITH A SMILE...

...KNOWING THAT HE WAS ABLE TO LIVE OUT HIS DREAM BESIDE HIS CAPTAIN.

IF OKITA SENSEI ENDS UP NEVER RETURNING...

...AM BUSHI.

FOR I TOO...

HUH?

IT'S KONDO SENSEI'S HAND-WRITING.

WHAT'S THIS DOING HERE?

As if it's begging to be read.

"...AND IN THE EVENT OF MY MISFORTUNE...

"...OKITA SHALL INHERIT THE *TEN'NEN RISHIN RYU*, AND THE MATTER IS NOT TO BE DISPUTED."

"...OKITA SHALL INHERIT THE *TEN'NEN RISHIN RYU*."

I AM TO INHERIT...

KONDO SENSEI?

CRAP! I CAN'T BELIEVE I DROPPED THAT!

HIJI-KATA-SAN...

YOU DIDN'T **READ** IT, DID YOU, SOJI!?

SNATCH

...

...BUT KONDO-SAN HAS HIS REASONS FOR WANTING TO KEEP YOU ALIVE.

← FAST-TALKING

I UNDERSTAND YOUR BEEF WITH ALL THIS...

YOU **BETTER NOT** HAVE READ THE LETTER!

THAT'S ALL I WANTED TO SAY. SEE YOU LATER.

I JUST DIDN'T WANT TO LEAVE TOMORROW WITH YOU FEELING ABANDONED. IT'D BOTHER MY CONSCIENCE.

...

*Confidentiality is a promise between men.

140

NO!

I HAVEN'T READ IT!

ARE YOU SURE, OKITA SENSEI!?!

WHAT? YOU'VE DECIDED *AGAINST* GOING?

THE NEXT DAY, KONDO AND COMPANY HEADED FOR HIROSHIMA.

ALTHOUGH THE ACCOMPANYING MEMBERS WERE ACTUALLY QUITE PROBLEMATIC.

I DON'T GET IT.

OH MY...

I JUST LOVE HIJIKATA-SAN!

THIS WAS OBVIOUSLY OF NO CONCERN TO THE GIRL.

KONDO HAS BEEN SENT TO HIROSHIMA WITH DIGNITARIES?!

IS THAT *TRUE*, UTSUMI?!

YES, KASHI-TARO-SAN.

AND IT'S NOT JUST AS SECURITY— HE'S TO CARRY OUT A SPECIAL MISSION OF INSPECTING CHOSHU.

KONDO! SINCE WHEN HAVE YOU BECOME SUCH A TRUSTWORTHY MAN TO THE BAKUFU?!

KAZE HIKARU IROHA KARUTA

"HO" ほ

HORETAKA DOUKAMO GOZONJINAI

submitted by Anko-san from Gifu

"IGNORANT EVEN ABOUT FALLING IN LOVE"

Feels so good

I wish I could be touching them all the time.

You're so cute, Kamiya-san

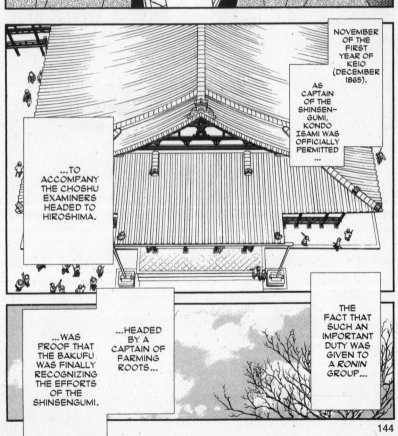

145

MY PATIENCE IS AT AN END...

...FOR COUNSELOR ITO TO VISIT THE CHOSHU, WHICH HE HATES.

YOU KNOW THAT THERE HAS TO BE SOME UNDERLYING REASON...

You made it too easy.

SO ITO KASHITARO WAS PERMITTED TO ACCOMPANY THE CAPTAIN...

...AND UNDER THE GUISE OF "SETTLING CRITICISM," ITO CHOSE MEMBERS WHOSE INFLUENCE WAS GUARANTEED..

DID YOU STICK HIM ON KONDO SENSEI FOR FEAR OF HIS NIGHTLY VISITS?

IT'S ALL I CAN DO TO REFRAIN FROM *KILLING THAT GUY!*

YOU'VE NO PERSEVER-ANCE!

HA HA HA!

I'M JUST A HEART-BREAKER!

I LOVE YOU!

...THE TWO MEN WHO BROUGHT HIM TO KYOTO AND MADE HIS SEEMINGLY UNOBTAINABLE DREAM A REALITY.

YAMAZAKI WAS UNWAVERINGLY DEVOTED AND LOYAL TO KONDO AND HIJIKATA...

YAMAZAKI WAS ALSO ONE OF THE MEN THAT SOJI TRUSTED THE MOST.

You're cheating again!

OKITA SENSEI!

IT'S ALMOST TIME FOR THE CAPTAIN'S DEPARTURE!

I'LL BE RIGHT THERE...

150

THEY PROBABLY HAVEN'T EVEN REACHED OSAKA.

I WONDER WHERE THEY ARE NOW...

I WILL OMIT THE DETAILS OF THE JOURNEY AS ONLY NERDS WOULD BE INTERESTED (*HEH*).

WAAAAAA

PROBABLY AT LEAST A MONTH.

I WONDER HOW LONG IT WILL BE UNTIL THEY RETURN...

DOWN

SHALL WE GO GET SOME SWEETS?

...

DOWN

155

156

157

WAIT.

HE SAID "OSA-KAYA"?

I FEEL LIKE I'VE HEARD OF AN "OSAKAYA."

HE MAY BE A MAN FROM A GLASS-WORKS.

I'VE ONLY SEEN IT AS BELLS AND HAIRPIECES.

I KNOW!

HOW RARE.

IT'S DEFINITELY A PIECE OF GLASS.

IT'S A WESTERN PHOTOGRAPHY STUDIO ON TERAMACHI STREET.

I'VE ONLY HEARD RUMORS.

YOU KNOW IT, SAITO-SAN?!

"YOHEI FROM OSAKAYA."

158

PHOTOGRAPHY'S SOMETHING THAT'S ONLY SPREAD AMONG THE WEALTHY.

HMPH.

OKITA SENSEI IS OF NO USE WHEN IT COMES TO THINGS LIKE THIS.

IT'S NO WONDER THAT OKITA-SAN DOESN'T KNOW OF IT.

Take that back!

FORCED INTO SILENCE— CANNOT SAY THAT KATAMORI-SAMA HAS ALREADY GOTTEN HIS PHOTO TAKEN ON NUMEROUS OCCASIONS.

THEN WHERE DID YOU LEARN OF IT?

HEY? WHY SO SILENT, SAITO-SAN? ♡

—...!

I HEARD SOMETHING ABOUT A MISTRESS ...

SO WHAT'S THE STORY?

↑ A blatant lie

WHA...

WHY DON'T YOU TELL US WHAT'S ON YOUR MIND?

160

162

WHAT DID THE MEN SAY WHEN THEY ATTACKED YOU YESTERDAY?!

WAIT! THAT'S WHAT WE'RE HERE FOR!

WHA!

HOW DID YOU JUST...

OKAY, OKAY! JUST LET ME GO! I'M GOING TO FALL!

YESTER-DAY...

I WAS GOING ABOUT TOWN MAKING DELIVERIES AND COLLECT-ING PAYMENT.

TOSS!

KYU-SAKU...

I JUST HAVE TO VISIT ONE FAVORED CUSTOM-ER.

I CAN DO THIS ON MY OWN. WHY DON'T YOU RUN THE ERRANDS I ASKED YOU TO AND THEN HEAD HOME?

YES, SIR! THANK YOU.

YOU'RE YOHEI OF OSAKAYA, AREN'T YOU?

166

DO YOU FEEL BETTER NOW?

HUFF HUFF HUFF HUFF

......

WHAT ?!

I'M SORRY IF YOU'VE MISUNDERSTOOD.

MY FATHER WAS A DOCTOR OF WESTERN MEDICINE. I AM WELL AWARE OF THE GREATNESS OF FOREIGN CULTURES.

MATSUMOTO HOGEN?!

AND WE HAVE A DOCTOR WHO TRAINED IN WESTERN MEDICINE IN NAGASAKI WHO WORKS AS OUR ATTENDING PHYSICIAN— MATSUMOTO HOGEN.

YES!

KILL ME IF YOU WISH!

WE DON'T WANT TO KILL YOU.

WE COMPLETELY AGREE.

THUD!

SHIVER SHIVER

THE DEAD OF WINTER

WOULD YOU MIND LENDING US SOMETHING TO DRY OURSELVES OFF WITH?

THAT'S TOTALLY NOT NECES- SARY.

I-I'M SO SORRY! HOW CAN I REPAY YOU?!

WHACK

KYU- SAKU!

YES, SIR!

FORGET THE WOODEN STAFF AND SALT! BRING ME TOWELS AND A CHANGE OF CLOTHES!

AND BRING ALL THE BRAZIERS IN THE HOUSE TO THE GUEST ROOM!

YES, SIR!

171

HA HA HA.

BUT WE'RE NOT DRESSED...

WITH OKITA SENSEI!?!

SWING!!

WOW!

PLEASE! YOU CAN USE ANYTHING!

DON'T WORRY!

I HAVE A WHOLE CLOSET FULL OF COSTUMES AND PROPS!

GRIN

HUH...? WHAT?

THEY'VE GOT WIGS, KAMIYA-SA...!

174

175

178

DON'T MOVE UNTIL I COUNT TO 15!

OKAY! ONE!

TWO!

THREE!

THE NEXT YEAR IN THE SECOND YEAR OF KEIO (1866)...

YOHEI OPENED A BRANCH OF HIS OSAKAYA IN GION.

HE WOULD MAKE HIS NAME AS A PHOTOGRAPHER WHO TOOK PICTURES OF MANY FIGURES IN KYOTO, NO MATTER WHAT A PERSON'S AFFILIATIONS WERE DURING THE END OF THE BAKUFU ERA.

BUT THERE IS NO RECORD OF WHO POSED FOR THIS SINGLE PHOTO.

HOWEVER, SOJI'S PLAYFULNESS THIS DAY ...

...WOULD COME BACK TO HAUNT HIM.

To Be Continued!

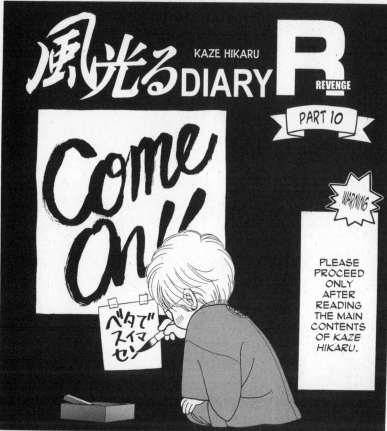

*Taped note: Sorry for the all black background.

GOOD, EH?

FAMILY CRESTS

YES, THE TOPIC OF THE DAY IS...

WOW... IT'S SO MOVING...

...THAT EVERYBODY CHECKS OUT THE ARTWORK IN SUCH DETAIL.

YOU'D BE SURPRISED AT THE NUMBER OF REQUESTS I GET...

...TO TALK ABOUT FAMILY CRESTS.

NOW FOR THE QUESTION!

TICK TOCK

TICK

TOCK

TIME'S UP IN 15 MINUTES!

WHAT?! I DIDN'T KNOW!

WHO WAS IT?!

THERE WAS ONE SHIEIKAN MEMBER WHOSE FAMILY CREST CHANGED HALFWAY THROUGH THE SERIES!

AREN'T YOU GOING TO EXPLAIN WHY YOU CHANGED IT?

PROFES-SOR VERSION

HOW CAN YOU MAKE A QUIZ OUT OF SUCH A SHAMEFUL FACT?!

HE HE

MANGA ARTIST VERSION

I JUST ARBI- TRARILY ASSIGNED ONE BEFORE I FOUND OUT WHAT IT REALLY WAS.

WELL... I JUST COULDN'T FINISH THE RESEARCH IN TIME FOR THE START OF THE SERIES...

IN THE FIRST VOLUME, IT WAS MARUNI KARIGANE ...

I selected this one from the family crest of someone with the last name Nagakura.

IN VOLUME 9, IT WAS CHANGED TO MATSUKA-WABISHI.

I took this from the headstone of Shinpachi's family in Hiroshima.

I FURTHER CONFESS TO THE FACT THAT HEISUKE'S CREST WAS RANDOMLY ASSIGNED.

You've got some balls.

I WANTED TO BE ACCURATE ON THE CRESTS FOR AT LEAST THE SHIEIKAN MEMBERS, SO I FORCED THE CHANGE.

I'M SORRY!

WOW... IT WAS NAGAKURA-SAN!

URGH

WHAT? REALLY?!

SO SINCE HEISUKE'S RUMORED TO BE A BASTARD CHILD, I SELECTED THE TODOTSUTA ASSOCIATED WITH THE TSU-HAN.

I HAVE YET TO COME ACROSS CONVINCING DOCUMEN-TATION...

THE REALITY OF THE SITUATION IS THAT IT'S DIFFICULT TO DETERMINE WHICH ONE OF THOSE IS HISTORICALLY ACCURATE.

AND SINCE I'M ALREADY ON THE SUBJECT, THERE ARE MANY DISCREPANCIES WITH REGARD TO FAMILY CRESTS BETWEEN INFORMATION PASSED BY WORD OF MOUTH, DOCUMENTS AND HEADSTONES.

Warning from the author: The name of the family crest itself also differs between books and authors.

INDEED...

HIDARI MITSU DOMOE (CLOCKWISE SWIRL) DOMINATES THE DOCUMENTS...

According to cenotaphs and tablets.

...but I don't want that to take over.

I want it to be accurate...

THIS WAS A DECISION I CAME TO AFTER MUCH MULLING OVER; SO PLEASE LET IT GO.

THEREFORE, WITH REGARD TO THE MOST FREQUENTLY RECEIVED COMPLAINT OF TOSHI'S CREST BEING REVERSED...

BUT THE HIJIKATA HEADSTONE AT THE FAMILY TEMPLE HAS A *MIGI MITSU DOMOE (COUNTER-CLOCKWISE SWIRL)*.

I WOULD LIKE TO BELIEVE THAT THIS FAMILY CREST, PROTECTED BY HIS ANCESTORS AND PRAISED BY HIS FANS, IS THE TRUE CREST!

WHICH IS WHY I WENT WITH IT FOR TOSHI IN *KAZE HIKARU*!

TOSHI'S GRAVE

HIJIKATA FAMILY

I'm doing my best, so please don't get mad.

I'm putting you in a shojo manga.

CONVERSELY, I ENDED UP BETRAYING KONDO-SAN'S FAMILY TEMPLE AND REDOING HIS CREST.

UPON FURTHER RESEARCH, I CAME TO FIND OUT THAT THERE WERE MANY SIMILAR BUT DIFFERENT CRESTS.

WHAT ?!

BUT IT CAME TO MY ATTENTION DURING THE SERIES THAT THERE WERE SLIGHT DIFFER-ENCES.

ACCORDING TO MY RESEARCH, THE CREST WAS DESCRIBED AS "A CIRCLE WITH THREE LINES," SO I THOUGHT NOTHING OF IT AS I DREW IT...

THE REAL ONE HAS THREE LINES *IN THE CIRCLE*?!

SHINSENGUMI!

THIS IS REALLY JUST FOR ME.

IT'S NOT AS IF ANY OF THE READERS HAVE NOTICED.

SO YOU'LL NOTICE THAT KONDO-SAN'S CREST HAS ALSO UNDERGONE MINOR CHANGES FROM VOLUME 6.

I CAN'T IGNORE SUCH A BIG CHARACTERISTIC!

SO MAYBE THIS ONE THAT HAS DIFFERENT THICKNESSES IS UNIQUE TO THE KONDO SHUSAI FAMILY?!

I ESPECIALLY OBSESSED OVER THE ONE THAT HAD DIFFERENT LINE THICKNESSES BUT FAILED TO FIND ANY FAMILY-CREST PICTURE BOOKS THAT SHOWED ONE.

It's okay. I'm having fun.

FAMILY CREST QUICK REFERENCE

FAMILY CRESTS
FAMILY CRESTS

Sketches by troop members...

Kondo-san's grave built by blank

The headstone of his adopted father, Shusai, in Edo.

MINE'S MARUNI HITOSTSU-BIKI!

I chose it because it resembles the scar on my stomach!

MINE IS MARUNI SHIHOUMO-TSUKO.

FOR-TUNATELY, I WAS ABLE TO DETERMINE THE OTHER MEMBERS' FAMILY CRESTS WITHOUT CONTRO-VERSY.

MINE IS MARUNI MIGIHANARE TACHI AOI.

MINE IS MARUNI HIRAI ZUTSU.

I WEAR THIS IN HONOR OF ANI-UE. IT'S CALLED HOSOWA NI KENZAKURA.

I ALSO GAVE SEI-CHAN A CREST.

BUT I DECIDED TO GO WITH IT, AS IT IS THE ONLY CREST KNOWN TO BE SAITO-SAN'S.

...THAT SAITO-SAN'S MARUNI KYUMAIZASA IS HISTORICALLY INACCURATE.

I'LL ALSO CONFESS...

I CAN'T GO INTO DETAIL HERE WITHOUT GIVING AWAY THE STORY!

AS LONG AS THE TOKUGAWA FAMILY'S AOIMON WAS AVOIDED, ANYTHING WAS GAME AT THIS TIME.

BUT YUMA CHANGED IT TO COMMEMORATE HIS JOINING THE SHINSENGUMI.

THE BACKGROUND STORY IS THAT THE TOMINAGA FAMILY CREST WAS ACTUALLY MATSUKOBISI.

See Volume 1 for details!

IT'S FUN TO FIND OUT WHAT YOUR FAMILY CREST IS, WHAT YOUR ANCESTORS' THOUGHTS WERE ON IT AND THE HISTORY BEHIND IT!

...who share crests with these ten men.

I'm sure there are some of you...

NATURALLY, THE WHOLE POINT OF THE CREST IS THAT IT IS INHERITED BY THE NEXT GENERATION!

Kaze Hikaru Diary R: The End

Decoding Kaze Hikaru

Kaze Hikaru is a historical drama based in 19th century Japan and thus contains some fairly mystifying terminology. In this glossary we'll break down archaic phrases, terms and other linguistic curiosities for you so that you can move through life with the smug assurance that you are indeed a know-it-all.

First and foremost, because *Kaze Hikaru* is a period story, we kept all character names in their traditional Japanese form—that is, family name followed by first name. For example, the character Okita Soji's family name is Okita and his personal name is Soji.

AKO-ROSHI:

The *ronin* (samurai) of Ako; featured in the immortal Kabuki play *Chushingura* (Loyalty), aka *47 Samurai.*

ANI-UE:

Literally, "brother above"; an honorific for an elder male sibling.

BAKUFU:

Literally, "tent government." Shogunate; the feudal, military government that dominated Japan for more than 200 years.

BUSHI:

A samurai or warrior (part of the compound word *bushido*, which means "way of the warrior").

CHICHI-UE:

An honorific suffix meaning "father above."

DO:

In kendo (a Japanese fencing sport that uses bamboo swords), a short way of describing the offensive single-hit strike *shikake waza ippon uchi.*

-HAN:

The same as the honorific *-san*, pronounced in the dialect of southern Japan.

-KUN:

An honorific suffix that indicates a difference in rank and title. The use of *-kun* is also a way of indicating familiarity and friendliness between students or compatriots.

MEN:

In the context of *Kaze Hikaru*, *men* refers to one of the "points" in kendo. It is a strike to the forehead and is considered a basic move.

MIBU-ROSHI:

A group of warriors that supports the Bakufu.

NE'E-SAN:

Can mean "older sister," "ma'am" or "miss."

NI'I-CHAN:

Short for *oni'i-san* or *oni'i-chan*, meaning older brother.

OKU-SAMA:

This is a polite way to refer to someone's wife. *Oku* means "deep" or "further back" and comes from the fact that wives (in affluent families) stayed hidden away in the back rooms of the house.

ONI:

Literally "ogre," this is Sei's nickname for Vice Captain Hijikata.

RANPO:

Medical science derived from the Dutch.

RONIN:

Masterless samurai.

RYO:

At the time, one *ryo* and two *bu* (four *bu* equaled roughly one *ryo*) were enough currency to support a family of five for an entire month.

-SAN:

An honorific suffix that carries the meaning of "Mr." or "Ms."

SENSEI:

A teacher, master or instructor.

SEPPUKU:

A ritualistic suicide that was considered a privilege of the nobility and samurai elite.

SONJO-HA:

Those loyal to the emperor and dedicated to the expulsion of foreigners from the country.

Previously, I said that the series theme was "touch" and received an influx of feedback saying, "What about volume 7 or 9?" To which my answer is, "Look closely!" They're only touching clothes!

So the seasonal word is "moon." Anyone familiar with Nijuroku Yamachi? It's a lunar-calendar festival to appreciate the moon that rises in the middle of the night on New Year's and the 26th of July. Legend has it that the Amida trinity of Amida Buddha, Kannon and Seishi could be seen in the moonlight on those nights. The people of Edo particularly used to enjoy the late night on July 26. And I'm sure among them were lovers who waited for the moon alone. This cover is just my imagination gone wild (heh).

Taeko Watanabe debuted as a manga artist in 1979 with her story *Waka-chan no Netsuai Jidai* (Love Struck Days of Waka). *Kaze Hikaru* is her longest-running series, but she has created a number of other popular series. Watanabe is a two-time winner of the prestigious Shogakukan Manga Award in the girls' category—her manga *Hajime-chan ga Ichiban!* (Hajime-chan Is Number One!) claimed the award in 1991, and *Kaze Hikaru* took it in 2003.

Watanabe read hundreds of historical sources to create *Kaze Hikaru*. She is from Tokyo.

KAZE HIKARU
VOL. 19
Shojo Beat Edition

STORY AND ART BY
TAEKO WATANABE

© 1997 Taeko WATANABE/Shogakukan
All rights reserved.
Original Japanese edition "KAZE HIKARU" published by SHOGAKUKAN Inc.

Translation & English Adaptation/Mai Ihara
Touch-up Art & Lettering/Rina Mapa
Design/Julie Behn
Editor/Jonathan Tarbox

Printed in Canada

Published by VIZ Media, LLC
P.O. Box 77010
San Francisco, CA 94107

10 9 8 7 6 5 4 3 2 1
First printing, August 2011

www.viz.com

www.shojobeat.com